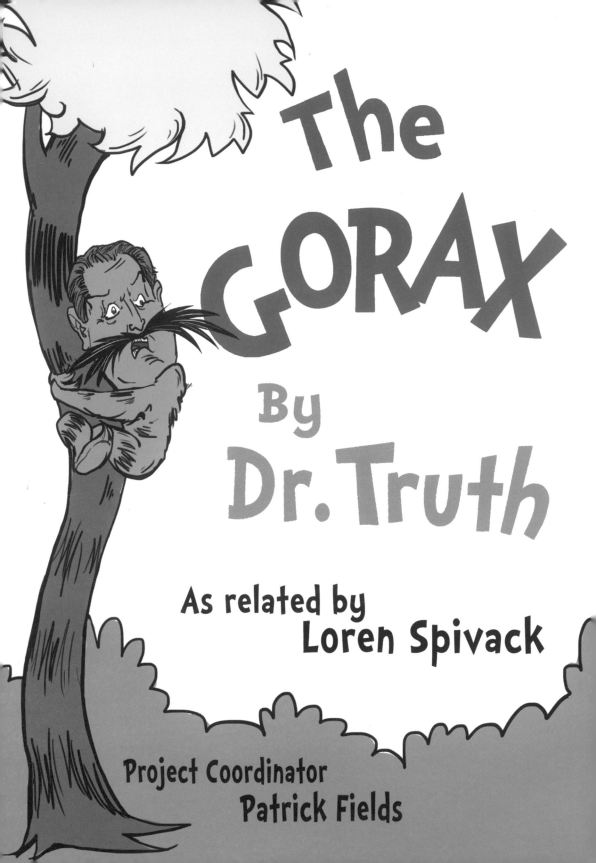

The GORAX

By
Dr. Truth

As related by
Loren Spivack

Project Coordinator
Patrick Fields

Dedicated to
James Watt
U.S. Secretary of the Interior, 1981-1983

Orders, including bulk wholesale orders, and other inquiries:

www.obamaparody.com
obamaparody@gmail.com
718-614-4411

"Phasing out the human race will solve every problem on earth, social and environmental. "

— Dave Forman, Founder of Earth First!

"Everything we have developed over the last 100 years should be destroyed."

— Pentti Linkola, Finnish Environmentalist and Writer

"We, in the green movement, aspire to a cultural model in which killing a forest will be considered more contemptible and more criminal than the sale of 6-year-old children to Asian brothels."

— Carl Amery, German Environmentalist

In the center of town where the bureaucrats dwell
And the Section 8 housing emits its own unique smell
And there's nothing to buy or even to sell,
Lies the corpse of the beaten Gorax.

And deep in the debris, behind a wrecked Chevy Volt
Past the burned out remains of the last urban revolt
You can see where he stood, just as long as he could,
Until someone gave the Gorax one heck of a jolt!

Who was the Gorax? And What did he do?
And why was he battered from his head to his shoe?
In the center of town, amidst urban decay,
Lives the Onepercentler. Ask him. He'll say.

You won't see the Onepercentler. He hides from the Feds.
And lives in an attic way overhead.
He suffers from headaches and ulcers and stress
And needs to make sure you're not IRS.
But he'll tell you the story like a whisper from heaven
For 15 Yuán, some bread that is leavened
And a shell for his great, great grandfather's 357.

He hides what you pay him so he won't have to declare
And be forced by the "99%" to "share it"
Because no one is allowed to reap profit from merit.

Then he lowers a Dixie cup on a cord
(Because cell phone taxes are too high to afford.)
And whispers "This is the safest way to relate
Information that is not approved by the state."

"Now I'll tell you," he says
Sounding slightly unnerved
"How the Gorax got the beating
He so richly deserved."

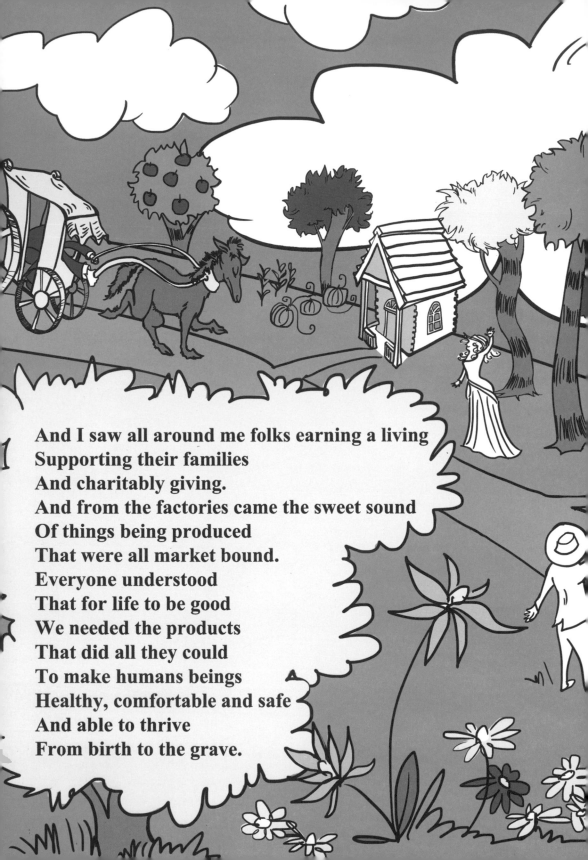

And I saw all around me folks earning a living
Supporting their families
And charitably giving.
And from the factories came the sweet sound
Of things being produced
That were all market bound.
Everyone understood
That for life to be good
We needed the products
That did all they could
To make humans beings
Healthy, comfortable and safe
And able to thrive
From birth to the grave.

I knew my ideas,
My brilliant ideas,
Would flourish and prosper
In surroundings like these.
And in return I could share
In the bounty that was there
That others had made
From their sweat, toil and care.

I had just built a factory right next to my house
When into my office came one pushy mouse.
So I set a small trap and soon heard a "snap"
And I said to myself, I guess that's a wrap!

But I was wrong! For all of a sudden a stretch limousine
Pulled up to my door and made quite a scene.
And out stepped an old man who looked awfully queer!

And he said, "That's offensive! I'll have to report you my dear!"

"Excuse me," I said, not certain I'd heard.
And he snapped, " 'Queer' is a culturally insensitive word.
The EEOC won't like it at all,
But I'll let you off easy, if you hire my friend Paul.
He'll give sensitivity training to your entire staff.
And he'll only charge you twenty grand and a half."

"Who are you?" I said, in confused disbelief
(Not knowing if he was serious or comic relief.)
"I am the Gorax, I speak for the mice!
And also the lice who live on the mice!
For the mice and the lice and the fleas cannot speak
And I have a government grant to stand up for the weak.
You killed this small rodent
With reckless malice and intent.
And I'm here to see that you quickly repent.
Moreover, parasites have been made homeless by you
And now they wander about without a clue what to do.
For you see, to a louse
That mouse was a house!"

Well I had heard quite enough from this unstable pest;
And no longer cared if this was real or in jest.

I said, "Listen here Gorax,
I don't care for your mice.
I don't care about fleas or maggots or lice.
I am trying to engage in productive employment
And better my fellow man's health, wealth and enjoyment.
And in the process, if you'll just let me be,
I'll make a better life for my whole family!
In fact my kids are helping out in the shop,
Cause they're hard-working too, just like their pop!"
"That's child labor!" The Gorax turned red.
"I'll have the Department of Labor down on your head!"
'Goodbye, Mr. Gorax," I said, holding the door.
"I haven't time for this nonsense anymore!"

Then he drove off in a thick cloud of smoke
And soon there was left no trace of the bloke.
But stuck in my mind were the words that he spoke.
I got to thinking what this annoying little man
Could actually do to ruin my plan,
And worsen the lives of everyone I knew.
And I wondered if we could stop him before he was through.

But there was work to be done
And a future to build.
And I couldn't waste an hour because some mouse had got killed.
So I hired more workers and expanded my line
And soon the whole town was doing just fine!
People enlarged their homes
And bought nicer cars
Took vacations abroad
And got their kids new guitars!
We built a standard of living
At which the whole world smiled
And a better future for every man, woman and child!

I had almost forgotten about that nut and his threat
Till one day he landed in his own private jet,
Outside my window, crushing some flowers.
"You're doing more damage to this environment of ours!"
He said, "I speak for the ozone
It's quickly depleting
Our studies have shown
As I keep repeating!
In fact, your factory has caused global warming
Due to the oil and coal that you're burning!"
I said, "You wouldn't be so warm if you try
Not wearing a fur coat in July!
And that oil and coal gives us power to make
Everything people need, for Pete's sake!
The earth has been cooling for the last several years
Completely debunking your irrational fears."

"Au contraire," he replied, "this July I fear
Will be hotter than any month this year!
And, if the trend of the last six months keeps going,
It soon will be 9000 degrees when it's snowing!
And global warming also causes global cooling, don't you know?
It does because I say it's so!
And worse than these both and more deadly by far
Is when global temperatures stay just where they are.
It all just goes to prove that I'm right!
And apparent normalcy means the danger has reached a new height!
100% of scientists who haven't been banned
For disagreeing with me
Take the same stand!
Oil and coal are gross and unclean.
They ruin the beautiful earth that is green!"

"They COME from the earth, you dimwit!" said I,
For I had quite enough of this crazy old guy.
And besides, your jet burns more fuel in an hour
Than my whole factory's use of power.
"Ah," said the Gorax, "let me give you a hint
Of how I erase my carbon footprint.
I pay thousands of pigmies 50 cents per day
To avoid all technology, where they live, far away.
So they languish in poverty and squalor
And I offset all my carbon use for pennies on the dollar.
I live in my 50,000 square foot palace, unbashful
And I use more electricity than the whole town of Nashville!
I can because I leave no footprint at all
Except when I step on capitalists, like you, with the gall
To defy my vision of a natural paradise for all.
And your factory here is engaged in production,
It's not at all like my job of instruction!
So we're going to have to give you a very strict quota
And measure your carbon use to the iota!
You know our country has just 2 percent
Of the whole world's oil reserves
So, we soon must relent
From using more than any such nation deserves!"

"Your statistics are years out of date.
We keep finding more oil at a fantastic rate.
Technology, like fracking, though no one can judge
Could make oil cheap -- I read it on Drudge!"
"I wish sometimes I had never invented
That Internet thing," he said, discontented.
"But we'll just make your 'fracking' illegal.
I'm sure it endangers some sub-species of eagle."
Here he took a deep breath and I could see he was going
To say much, much more before thinking of slowing.
"I also speak for the grass
And it doesn't like being mowed.
And I speak for the flowers
On the side of the road.
They don't want you driving around anymore."
Then he opened the door
And in came a dozen bureaucrats or more.

"I also speak for the trees that your business uses.
And we need to stop you, before you commit more abuses.
You'll cut them all down! Every last one!"
"That's illogical," I said, "And not how business is run.
Who would be so crazy as to destroy all the wood?
That's necessary for his livelihood.
We keep planting more
Cause we want to persist
And keep making money
Hand over fist!"
"Well, I speak for your workers
They want free insurance.
And I speak for investors
So we'll test your endurance
With financial regulations
Which we're here to impose
After we audit you down to your toes."
"But I'll be out of business!
I can't possibly continue
With all these restrictions,
And I'm sure there's more in you!"
"That will help the environment,"
The old Gorax laughed.
"After years of exploitation it's time you got the shaft!
You've been making much more than is your fair share
And everyone will be happy to see one less millionaire.
'Cause I speak for the poor, though I never met any
And I'm one of the elect who only care for the many."

"Don't forget that for 40 years," said the Gorax,
"We've been running the schools!"
"But what will the people
Do for a job,
If business can't function?"
I said witha sob.
"They can come work for me
And help run the state.
I have plenty of openings
And much to regulate."
"What will people eat is nothing is made?
And the government is the only place to get paid?"

"You're so wrong," said the Gorax.
"Look, there's the Fed.
They allow us to keep our budget
Perpetually in the red.
And THEY produce money
Which is the greatest of deeds.
Because green pieces of paper are what everyone needs!

Then I don't know what got in me
And I don't know why
But I just couldn't take
One more word from this guy.
I curled up my fist
(You know how it goes)
And I punched him as hard
As I could in the nose!
The whole street fell silent
I felt frozen in place
With the Gorax clutching
What remained of his face.

Then from all corners
People started to come.
And I was sure it was the end
I was sure I was done.

When I forced myself, finally, to open my eyes,
Well, you'll never believe my great, great surprise!
One after another my neighbors and friends,
My former employees
From as far away as South Bend
Came up to the Gorax and they hit him too!
They beat him and punched him
Till he was black and blue.

They said, "That's for my job!"
And, "That's for my house!"
"And that's for the job that was held by my spouse!"
"That's for what you did to my third cousin Dinah
When you forced them to relocate her factory to China!"
"That's for John Maynard Keynes and his stimulus bunk,
That's for the standard of living you've shrunk!"
"That's for destroying the true basis of wealth!"
"That's for undermining our constitution by stealth!"

When they got through with the Gorax
There wasn't much left.
So we all crept away
We were silent and deft.
Then I took a few stones from my factory lot
And I spelled out a word that's worth more than I've got.
A word that means everything to one who has lost
Because 'FREEDOM' is worth it, whatever the cost!

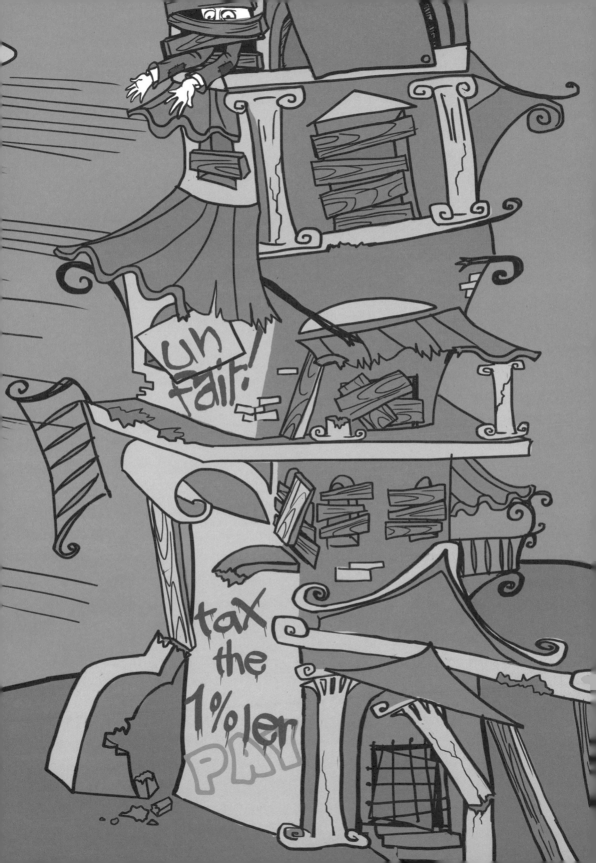

"So, catch!" calls the Onepercentler.
He lets something fall.
It's the Constitution,
The last copy of all.
"You're in charge of our heritage,
Don't let us down.
Teach your friends and your children
Spread it around.
Stand up for your freedom against socialist schemers,
Environmentalist wackos
And utopian dreamers.
Don't let crack-pot economists
And left-wing politicians
Get in the way of your most vital mission.
If we can pry our country from these political hacks
Maybe our prosperity and all will come back."